# *It's for You, Snoopy*

Charles M. Schulz

Selected cartoons from
*Sunday's Fun Day, Charlie Brown*, Vol. 1

**A FAWCETT CREST BOOK**

Fawcett Publications, Inc., Greenwich, Conn.

*IT'S FOR YOU, SNOOPY*

This book, prepared especially for Fawcett Publications, Inc., comprises the first half of *SUNDAY'S FUN DAY, CHARLIE BROWN*, and is reprinted by arrangement with Holt, Rinehart & Winston, Inc.

Copyright © 1962, 1963, 1964, 1965 by
United Feature Syndicate, Inc.

All rights reserved, including the right to reproduce this book or portions thereof in any form.

Printed in the United States of America
May 1971

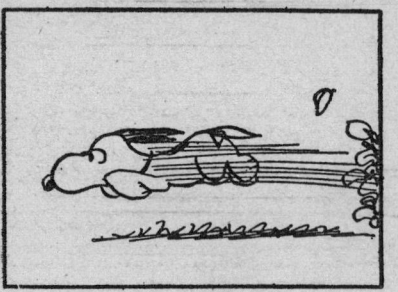

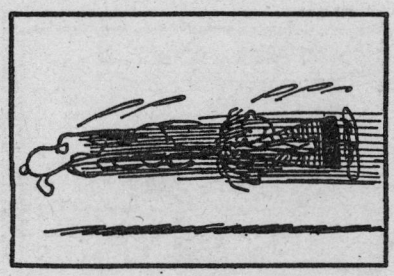
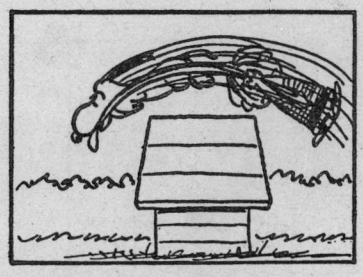

!
OH, OH! I CAN SEE WHAT'S COMING!
I MUST BE OUT OF MY MIND...
NOW I HAVE TO FIND SOME PLACE ELSE TO STAY UNTIL THOSE STUPID EGGS HATCH, AND THE BABY BIRDS LEARN HOW TO FLY... GOOD GRIEF!
I'M THE KIND THAT PEOPLE JUST NATURALLY TAKE ADVANTAGE OF...

EXCUSE ME, SNOOPY.. I HAVE TO GET THE MAIL..
THAT'S QUITE ALL RIGHT
WHAT A STUPID WAY TO LIVE!
I WONDER IF THOSE BABY BIRDS HAVE HATCHED YET..
I NEED TO GET MY OWN HOME BACK..I DON'T CARE FOR THIS LIVING OUT
THEY'RE HERE! THEY'VE BEEN BORN!

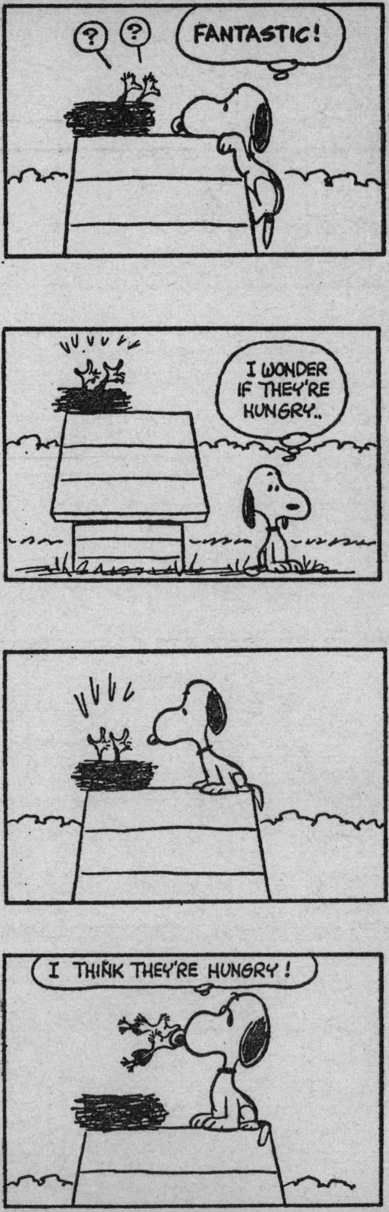
?
?
FANTASTIC!
I WONDER IF THEY'RE HUNGRY..
I THINK THEY'RE HUNGRY!

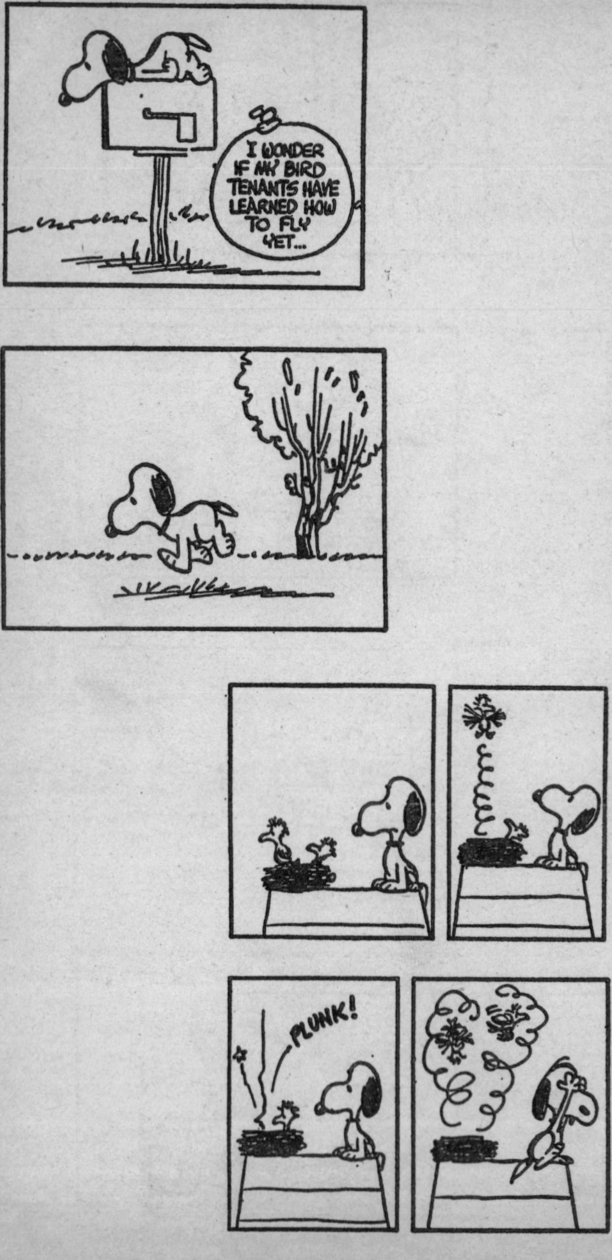
I WONDER IF MY BIRD TENANTS HAVE LEARNED HOW TO FLY YET...
PLUNK!

GO, BIRDS, GO! DON'T GIVE UP! GO! GO! GO!
GO! GO! GO! GO! GO!
WHOOPS!
STUPID BIRDS!

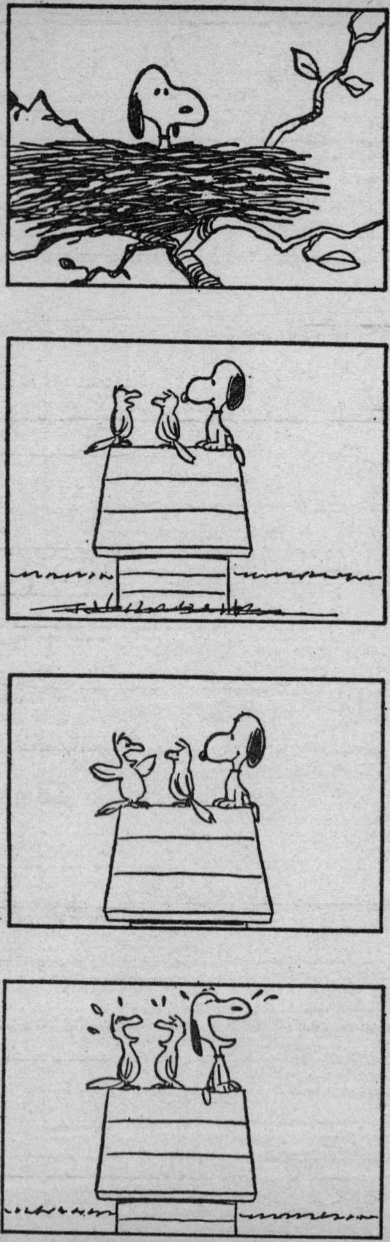

KLUNK!
I ALWAYS FORGET...ONLY BIRDS OF A FEATHER FLOCK TOGETHER!

AH! A PERFECT DAY!
ALL RIGHT, RISE AN'SHINE! IT'S RABBIT-CHASING TIME!!
OH, GOOD GRIEF!
THE SNOW IS FRESH AND THE AIR IS CLEAR...I PREDICT WE'LL SEE LOTS OF GAME!
HOW CAN YOU CHASE RABBITS IN THE MIDDLE OF THE NIGHT?

WE'LL START HERE...THIS IS A BIG FIELD, AND YOU SHOULD BE ABLE TO PICK UP THE SCENT WITHOUT...
Z
WAKE UP!

OKAY! HERE WE GO!!
SNIF SNIF SNIF SNIF

SNIF SNIF SNIF SNIF SNIF
I GUESS WERE NOT GOING TO FIND ANY, SNOOPY, BUT AT LEAST WE TRIED...

EVEN THOUGH YOU'VE FAILED, IT ALWAYS MAKES YOU FEEL BETTER WHEN YOU KNOW YOU'VE DONE YOUR BEST!
I'D HATE TO DISILLUSION HER, BUT I DON'T EVEN KNOW WHAT A RABBIT SMELLS LIKE!

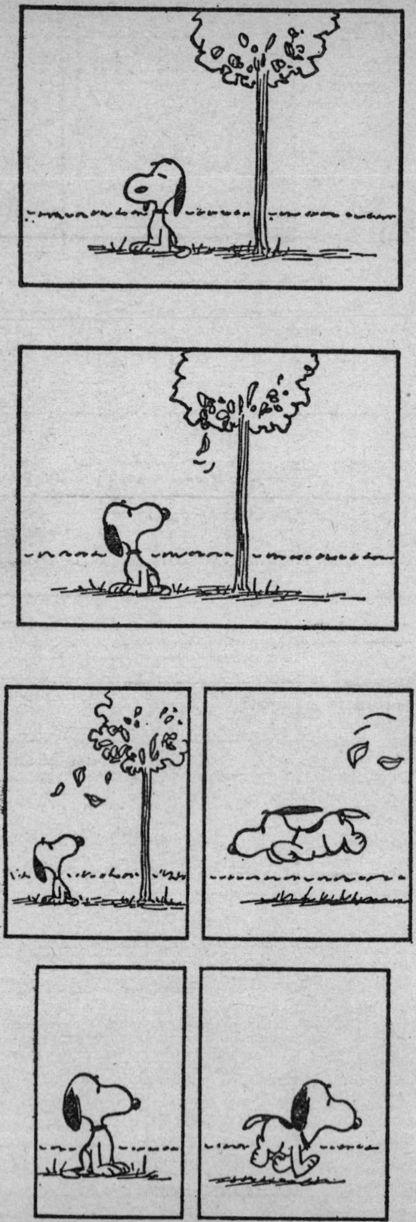

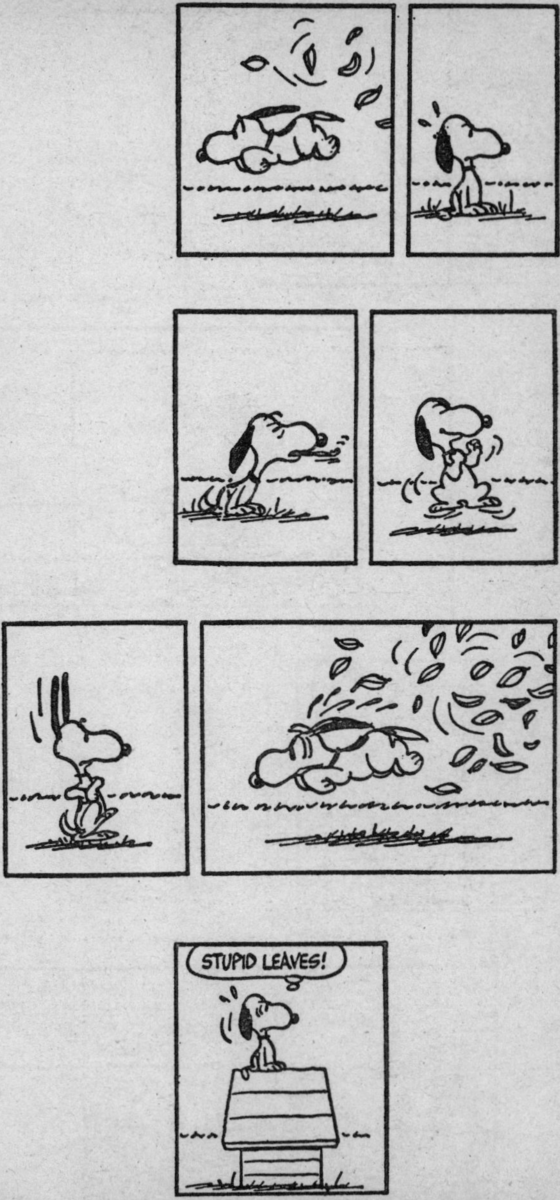
STUPID LEAVES!

SIT UP, SNOOPY, AND I'LL GIVE YOU A NICE PIECE OF CANDY...
HUMPF!
"SIT UP, SNOOPY, AND I'LL GIVE YOU A NICE PIECE OF CANDY."....PHOOEY! WHO NEEDS IT?!

I GET SICK AND TIRED OF THEIR CONDESCENDING ATTITUDE!
WHY SHOULD I HAVE TO BEG FOR EVERYTHING? I'M AS GOOD AS THEY ARE! I DON'T NEED THEM! I CAN GET ALONG BY MYSELF!
OR CAN I ?

WHAT'S THIS?
HAVEN'T YOU HEARD?
HE'S STANDING ON HIS HEAD AS PART OF A PROTEST MOVEMENT!
HE'S PROTESTING THE WAY HUMANS ARE RUINING THE WORLD FOR ALL THE ANIMALS...

HE'S GOING TO STAND ON HIS HEAD UNTIL THESE WRONGS HAVE BEEN RIGHTED!
HE FEELS THAT THIS IS ONE WAY OF ATTRACTING ATTENTION TO THE ANIMALS' PLIGHT..
WELL? WHAT DO YOU THINK?
PRETTY STUPID!
!
THAT'S WHAT I THOUGHT ALL ALONG, BUT I DIDN'T WANT TO SAY ANYTHING!

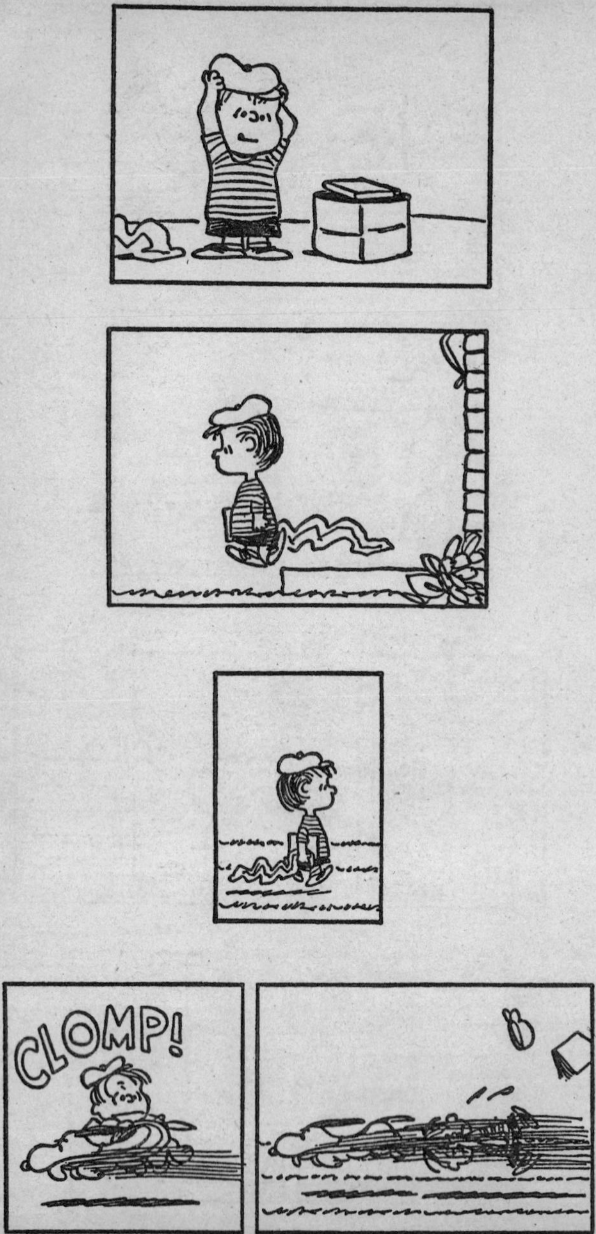
CLOMP!

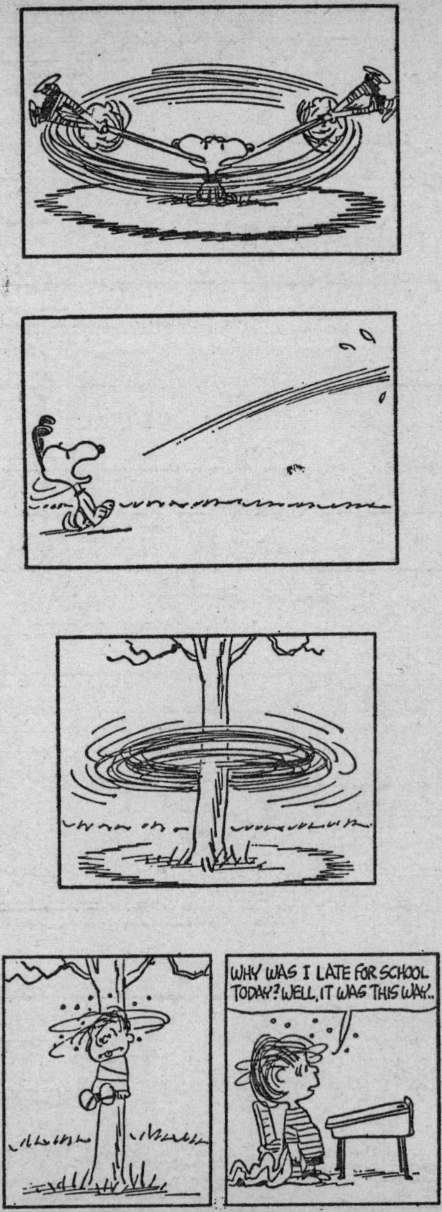
WHY WAS I LATE FOR SCHOOL TODAY? WELL, IT WAS THIS WAY..

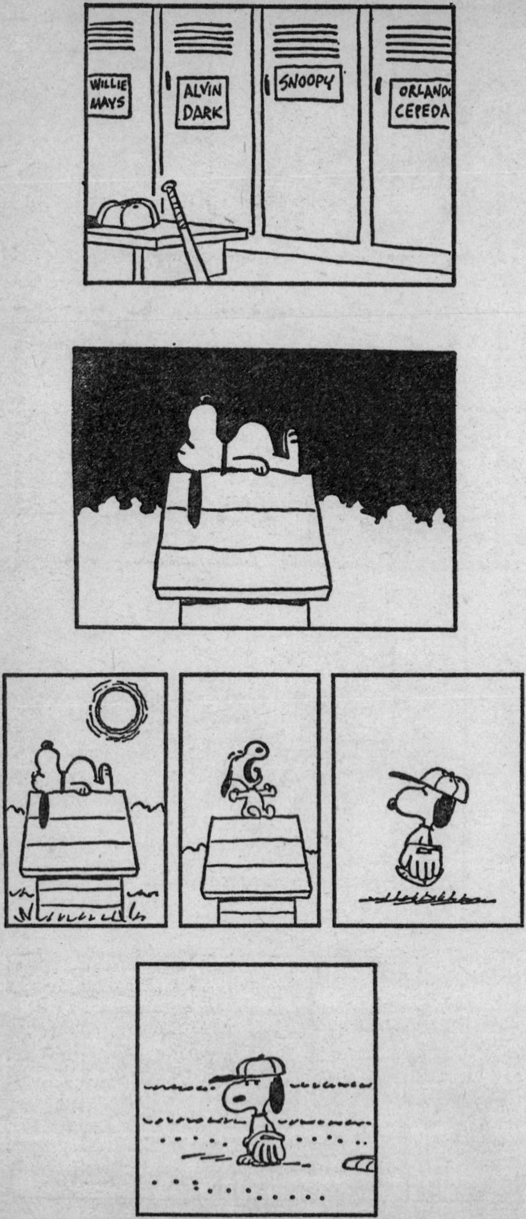
WILLIE MAYS
ALVIN DARK
SNOOPY
ORLANDO CEPEDA

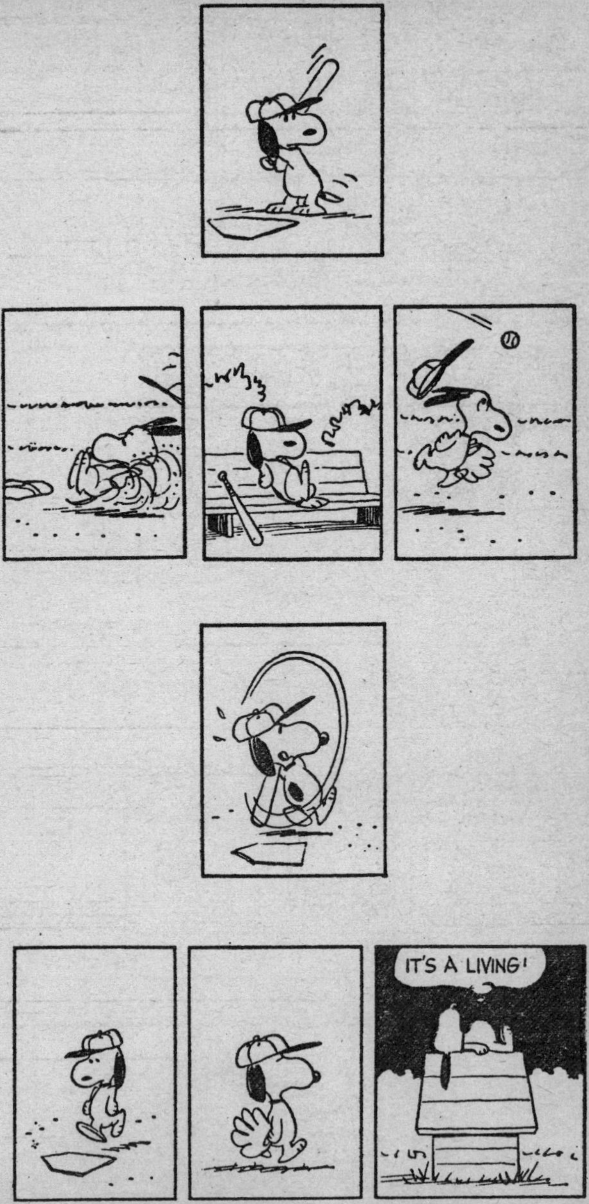
IT'S A LIVING!

HEY, MANAGER.. WE HAVE A PROBLEM!
I'M USED TO THAT..
MANAGER
WE'RE MISSING SECOND BASE TODAY SO I THOUGHT WE COULD USE SNOOPY'S DISH..
I GUESS THAT'LL DO ALL RIGHT FOR PRACTICE
MANAGER
WAP!

POW

THIS IS GOING TO BE ONE OF THOSE DAYS WHEN WE GET NOTHING BUT SINGLES

BUBBLE GUM
Players pictures averages
1¢
ARE YOU GOING TO BUY COMIC BOOKS CHARLIE BROWN?
NOT ON YOUR LIFE!
SEE THIS FIVE DOLLARS? I'M GOING TO SPEND IT ALL ON BUBBLE GUM CARDS! I'VE **GOT** TO GET A PICTURE OF **JOE SHLABOTNIK**!
FIVE DOLLARS' WORTH OF BUBBLE GUM, PLEASE!
I'D DO ANYTHING TO GET A JOE SHLABOTNIK BUBBLE GUM CARD.. HE'S MY HERO...

FIVE DOLLARS' WORTH OF BUBBLE GUM, AND NOT ONE JOE SHLABOTNIK!
A PENNY'S WORTH OF BUBBLE GUM, PLEASE..
WELL, WHAT DO YOU KNOW....JOE SHLABOTNIK!

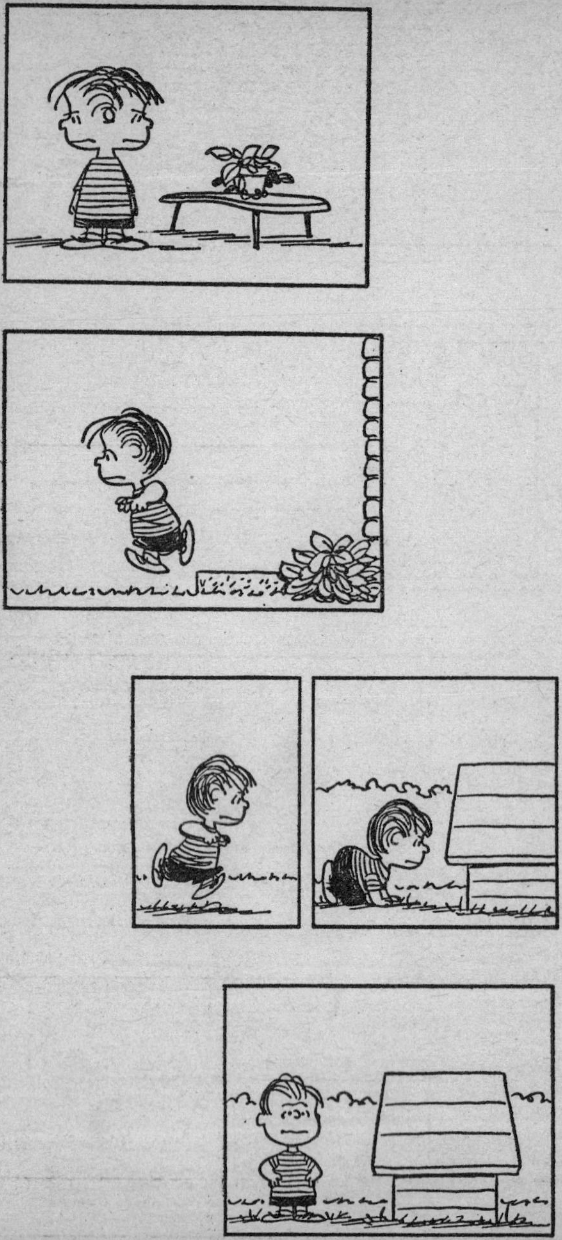

GOLLY! HAVE YOU EVER SEEN SO MANY SNAKES AND LIZARDS IN ALL YOUR LIFE?!! NO...AND SPIDERS, TOO... SPIDERS, TOO? YEAH, SNAKES AND LIZARDS AND SPIDERS!
?
AND THEY'RE ALL HEADED THIS WAY, YOU SAY? YEAH, THERE'S A WHOLE FLOCK OF 'EM...ALL HEADED THIS WAY...CREEPING AND CRAWLING... SNAKES AN' LIZARDS AN'..
!
!!

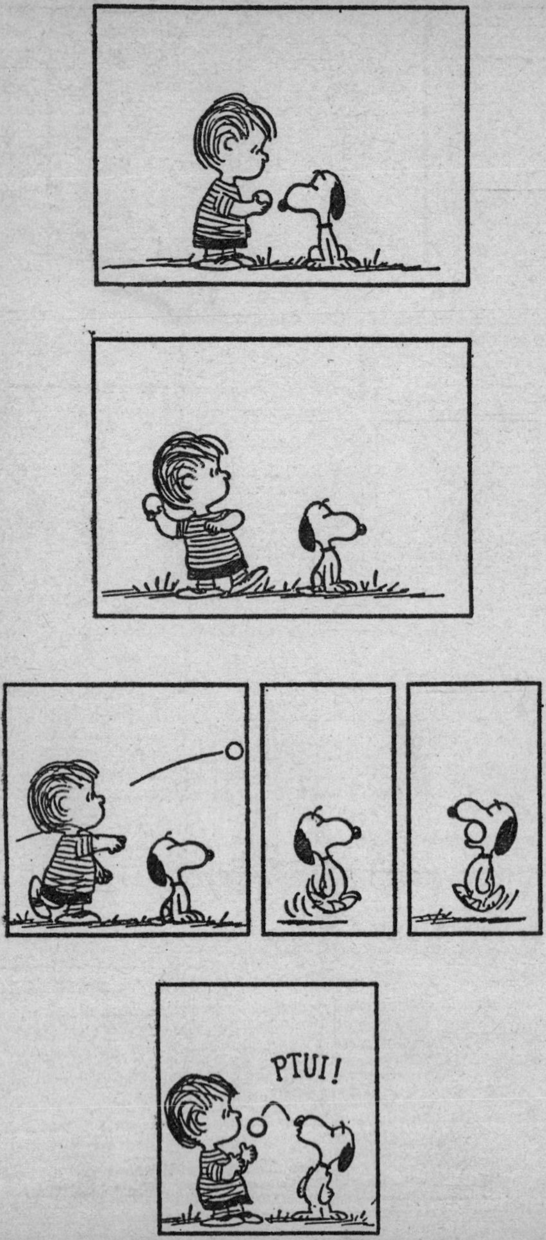
PTUI!

PTUI!
UNTIL IT IS DEMONSTRATED, ONE FORGETS THE REALLY GREAT DIFFERENCE THAT EXISTS BETWEEN THE MERELY COMPETENT AMATEUR AND THE VERY EXPERT PROFESSIONAL

I FEEL STRANGE..
I FEEL VERY LOVING TODAY...I THINK I'LL KISS SOMEBODY ON THE CHEEK!
SMACK!

AAUGH! SOMEBODY GET ME SOME SOAP AND WATER! I'VE JUST BEEN KISSED BY A DOG!
GET HOT WATER! GET SOME DISINFECTANT! GET SOME IODINE!
GOOD GRIEF!
NEXT TIME I'LL BITE HER ON THE LEG!

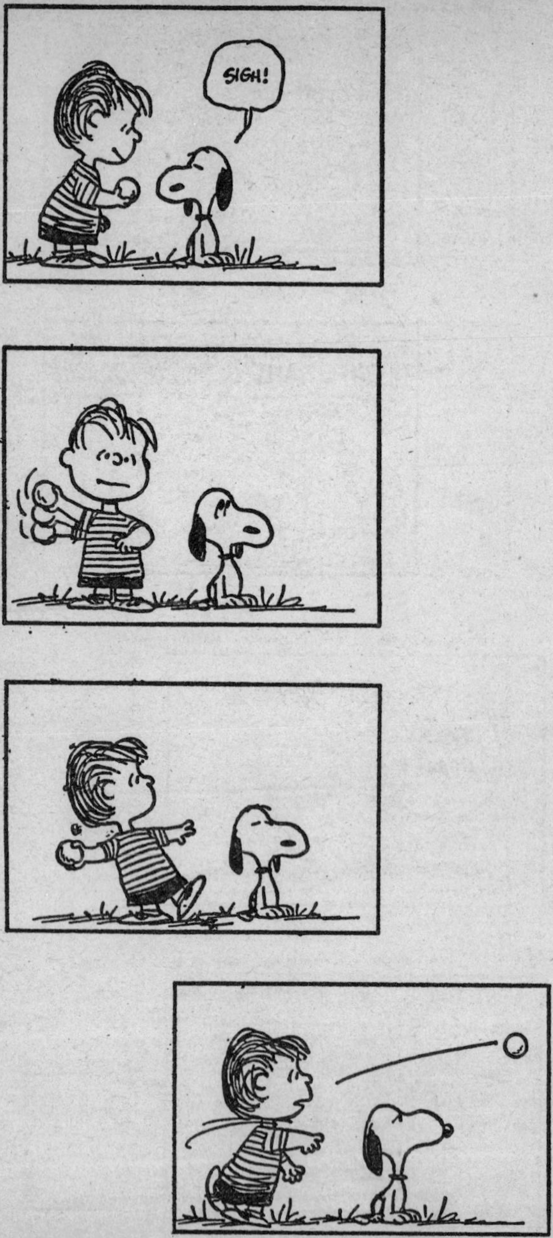
SIGH!

SLOBBER SLOBBER
DROOL
DRIP
SLOBBER SLOBBER
DROOL
DRIP
BLEAH!
THAT ENDED THAT GAME IN A HURRY!

HMM..
THAT'S A SAD STORY..
SO SUDDENLY YOU'RE WITHOUT A HOME..WHY DON'T YOU STAY WITH ME?
?

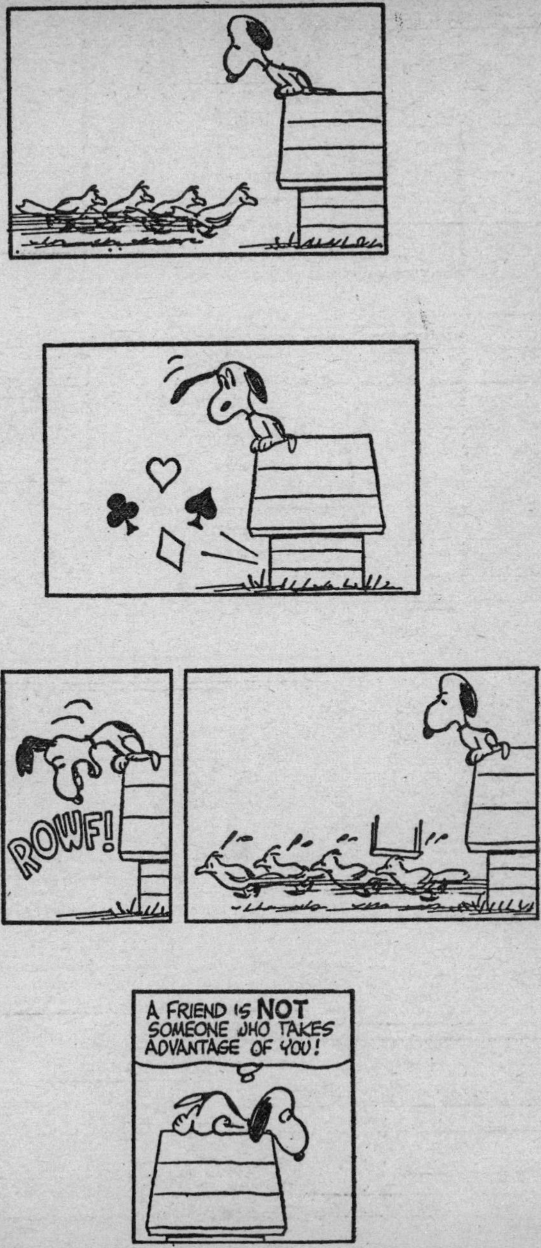
ROWF!
A FRIEND IS NOT SOMEONE WHO TAKES ADVANTAGE OF YOU!

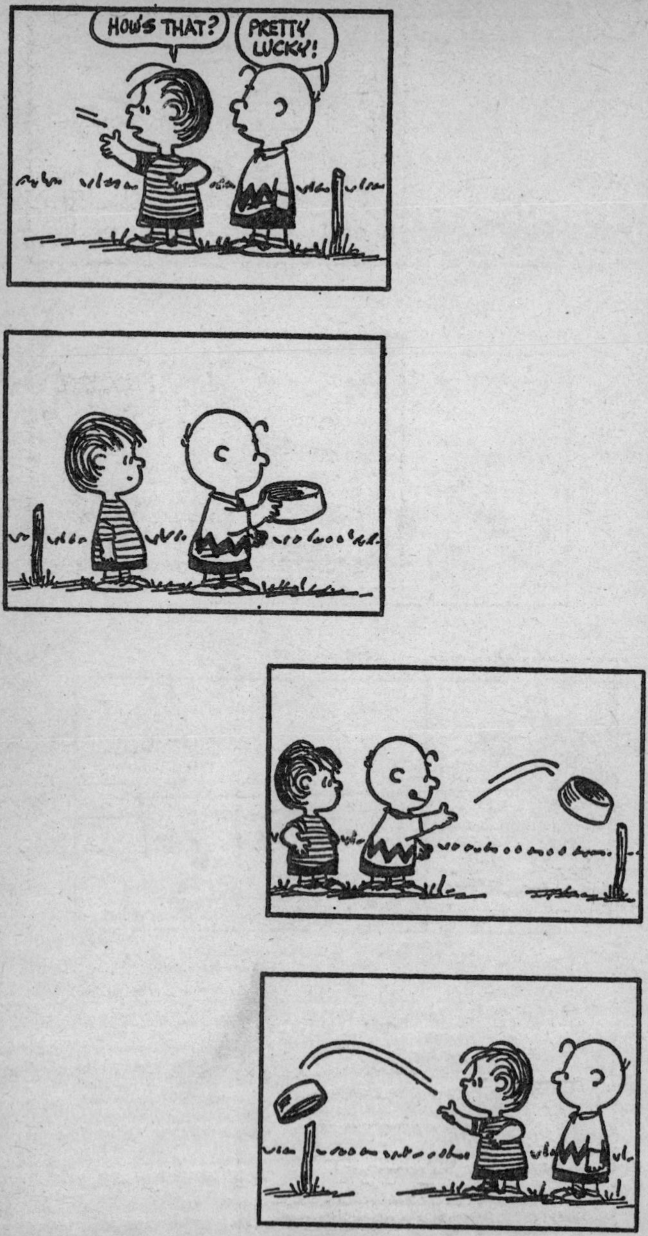
HOW'S THAT?
PRETTY LUCKY!

AHEM
WHAT CAN YOU DO WITH PEOPLE WHO REFUSE TO RECOGNIZE THE SANCTITY OF THE SUPPER DISH?

good grief!
TWELVE ERRORS IN ONE INNING!
WHAT A TEAM I'VE GOT!
ALL RIGHT, HOW ABOUT GIVING ME A LITTLE SUPPORT OUT THERE? I CAN'T WIN THIS GAME BY MYSELF, YOU KNOW!

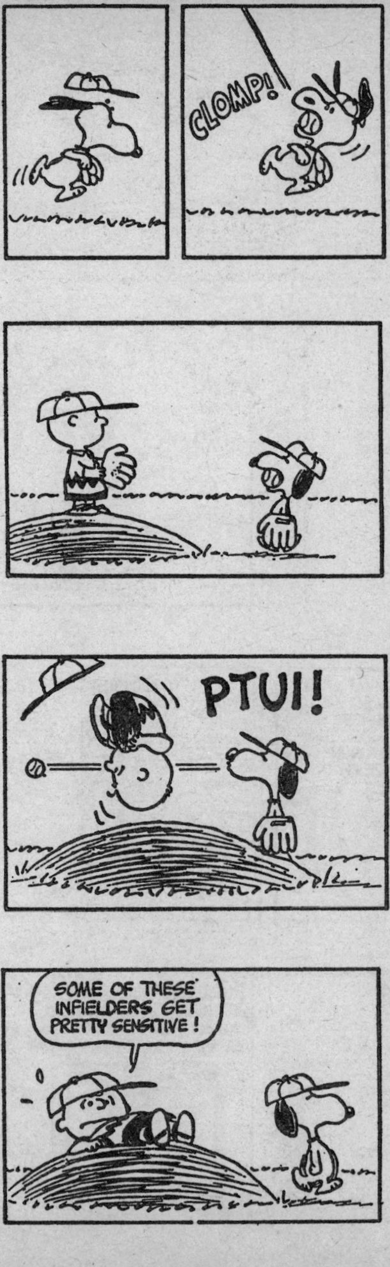
CLOMP!
PTUI!
SOME OF THESE INFIELDERS GET PRETTY SENSITIVE !

SCHOOL ZONE
* SIGH *
THERE'S THAT LITTLE RED-HAIRED GIRL WALKING HOME FROM SCHOOL...JUST THINK...I'M WALKING ON THE SAME SIDEWALK SHE'S WALKING ON
OF COURSE, I'M WALKING SEVEN BLOCKS BEHIND HER, BUT I'M WALKING ON THE VERY SAME SIDEWALK
I WISH I WERE WALKING WITH HER...I WISH I WERE WALKING RIGHT BESIDE HER, AND WE WERE TALKING
SHE WENT INTO THAT NICE HOUSE! SO THAT'S WHERE SHE LIVES...AND THERE'S THE DOOR SHE WENT IN...

I WISH SHE'D INVITE ME OVER TO HER HOUSE SOME TIME.. I WISH SHE'D COME UP TO ME, AND SAY, "WHY DON'T YOU COME OVER TO MY HOUSE AFTER SCHOOL, CHARLIE BROWN?"
THERE SHE IS AGAIN..SHE WENT INTO THE BACKYARD, AND SHE'S SWINGING ON HER SWING-SET...

WE COULD WALK HOME FROM SCHOOL TOGETHER, AND THEN WE COULD SWING ON HER SWING-SET...
BOY, WHAT A BLOCKHEAD I AM! I'LL NEVER GET TO SWING WITH HER! I'LL NEVER GET TO WALK WITH HER! I'LL NEVER EVEN GET TO SAY ONE WORD TO HER!

ALL I GET TO DO IS WALK HOME FROM SCHOOL BY MYSELF, AND...
OH, HI, SNOOPY

YOU'RE NOT MUCH OF A SUBSTITUTE FOR A LITTLE RED-HAIRED GIRL
QUITE OFTEN LATELY I HAVE THE FEELING I DON'T KNOW WHAT'S GOING ON...

Linus Van Pelt
ENGLISH I

SNOOPY, I'D LIKE TO READ YOU A STORY I'VE WRITTEN AND ILLUSTRATED FOR SCHOOL...

"ONCE THERE WAS A LITTLE GIRL WHO HAD A HEADACHE."

HER MOM GAVE HER SOME PILLS, BUT THEY DIDN'T HELP. HER MOM THEN TOOK HER TO THE DOCTOR.

"THE DOCTOR WAS UNABLE TO FIND ANYTHING WRONG."
?
"THIS IS A MYSTERIOUS CASE," HE SAID.
"THE LITTLE GIRL'S MOTHER TOOK HER HOME, AND PUT HER TO BED... HER HEAD THROBBED."
"HER LITTLE BROTHER CAME IN, AND SAID, 'MAYBE YOUR EARS ARE TOO TIGHT.'"
SO HE LOOSENED EACH EAR ONE TURN BACK. HER HEADACHE SUDDENLY STOPPED, AND SHE NEVER HAD ANOTHER HEADACHE AGAIN.
!
I GUESS HE DIDN'T LIKE IT.... THAT WAS HIS "GOOD LUCK, YOU'RE GOING TO NEED IT" HANDSHAKE!

TEETH MARKS
AAUGH!
?
HAVE YOU BEEN CHEWING ON MY NEW BAT ?!!
WHAT SORT OF A STUPID DOG ARE YOU? DON'T YOU HAVE ANY MORE SENSE THAN TO CHEW ON A BASEBALL BAT ?!

IF YOU HAVE TO CHEW ON SOMETHING, CAN'T YOU FIND A STICK OR A BONE OR A FENCE OR SOMETHING? DO YOU HAVE TO RUIN A GOOD BASEBALL BAT?! WHY CAN'T YOU...
HE DIDN'T CHEW ON YOUR BAT..I USED IT TO HIT ROCKS!
DO YOU WANT A BITE?

I'LL HOLD THE BALL, AND YOU KICK IT...
OH, BROTHER!
I DON'T MIND YOUR DISHONESTY HALF AS MUCH AS I MIND YOUR OPINION OF ME... YOU MUST THINK I'M REALLY STUPID...
I KNOW YOU DON'T TRUST ME, CHARLIE BROWN... YOU THINK THAT I'M GOING TO PULL THIS FOOTBALL AWAY WHEN YOU COME RUNNING UP TO KICK IT...
WELL, HERE'S A SIGNED DOCUMENT TESTIFYING THAT I PROMISE NOT TO DO IT...
?
IT IS SIGNED! IT'S A SIGNED DOCUMENT!

I GUESS IF YOU HAVE A SIGNED DOCUMENT IN YOUR POSSESSION, YOU CAN'T GO WRONG...THIS YEAR I'M REALLY GOING TO KICK THAT FOOTBALL!
AAUGH!
WUMP!
PECULIAR THING ABOUT THIS DOCUMENT.. IT WAS NEVER NOTARIZED!
*SIGH*

WHAT ONE CANNOT EAT NOW, ONE MUST BURY FOR LATER CONSUMPTION..
..IT'S A REAL MYSTERY..
HOW DOES HE DO IT?

HOW CAN HE BURY A BONE TODAY, AND THEN FIND IT THREE MONTHS FROM NOW..ESPECIALLY UNDER ALL THIS SNOW?!
I JUST DON'T UNDERSTAND..
IT'S VERY SIMPLE..
I HAVE "TOTAL RECALL"!

DO I HEAR MY NAME BEING CALLED?
AM I BEING PAGED?
DO I HEAR A CAR MOTOR?
I AM!
I DO!
C'MON, SNOOPY! AT-A-BOY!
JUMP RIGHT IN! THERE YOU GO!

HA! HE DID IT!! I OPENED THE CAR DOOR, AND HE JUMPED RIGHT IN!
?
WE TRAPPED HIM WITHOUT A STRUGGLE....
MY DAD'S TAKING HIM DOWN TO THE VET FOR A RABIES SHOT...
RATS! I THOUGHT WE WERE GOING OUT TO DINNER!

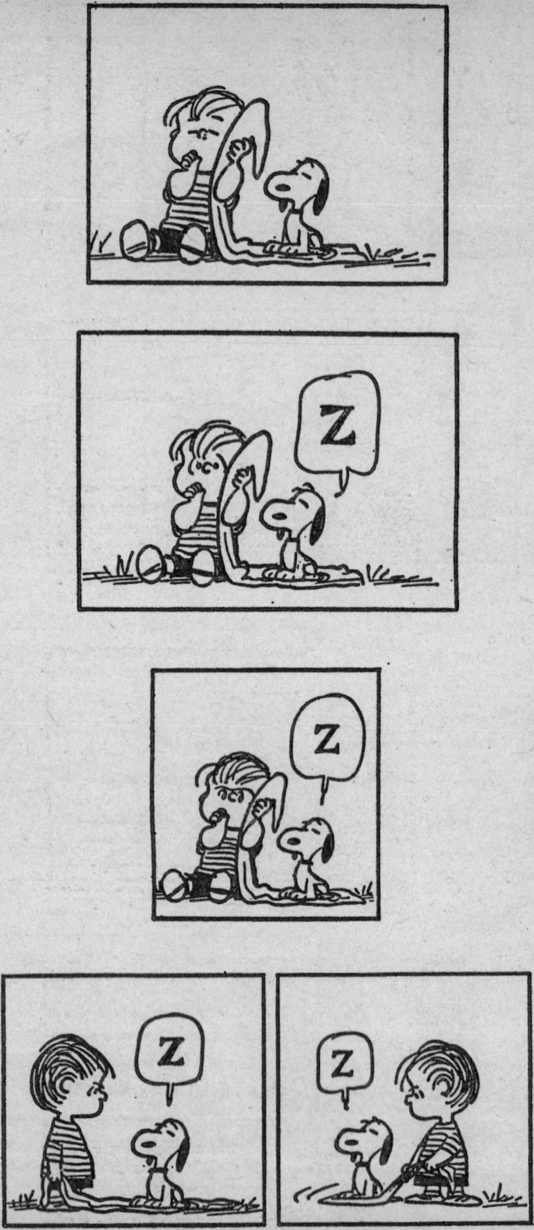
Z
Z
Z
Z

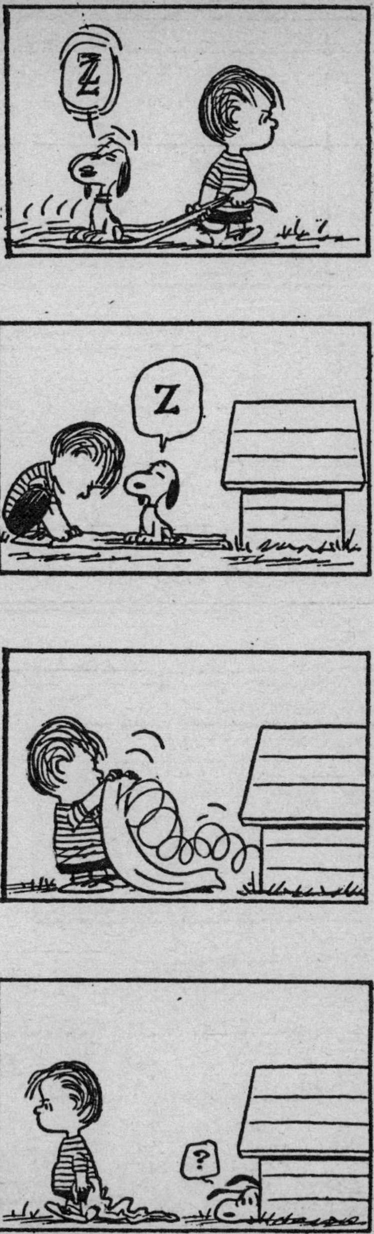
Z
Z
?

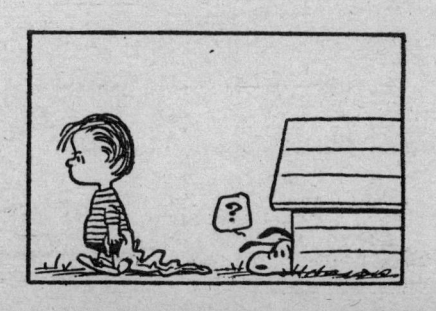

HERE'S THE FIERCE MOUNTAIN LION WAITING FOR HIS VICTIM...

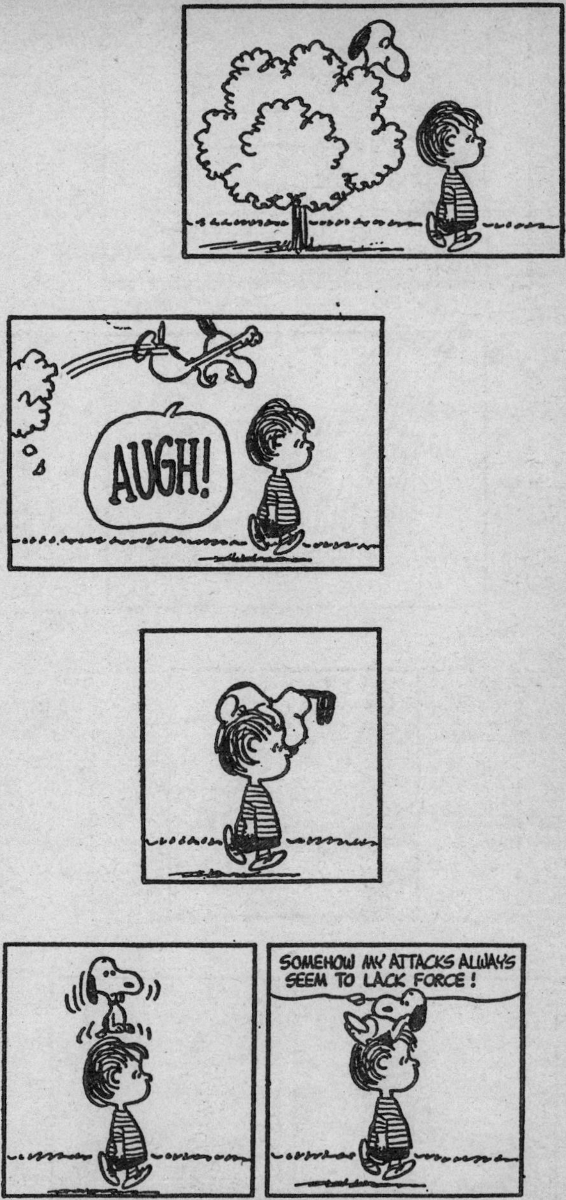
AUGH!
SOMEHOW MY ATTACKS ALWAYS SEEM TO LACK FORCE!

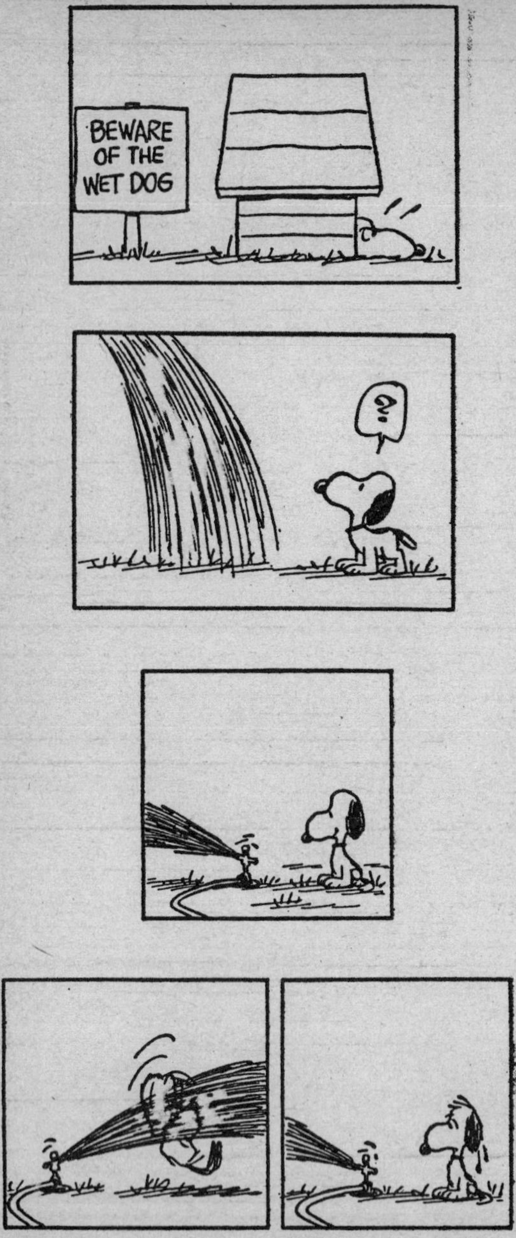
BEWARE OF THE WET DOG
?

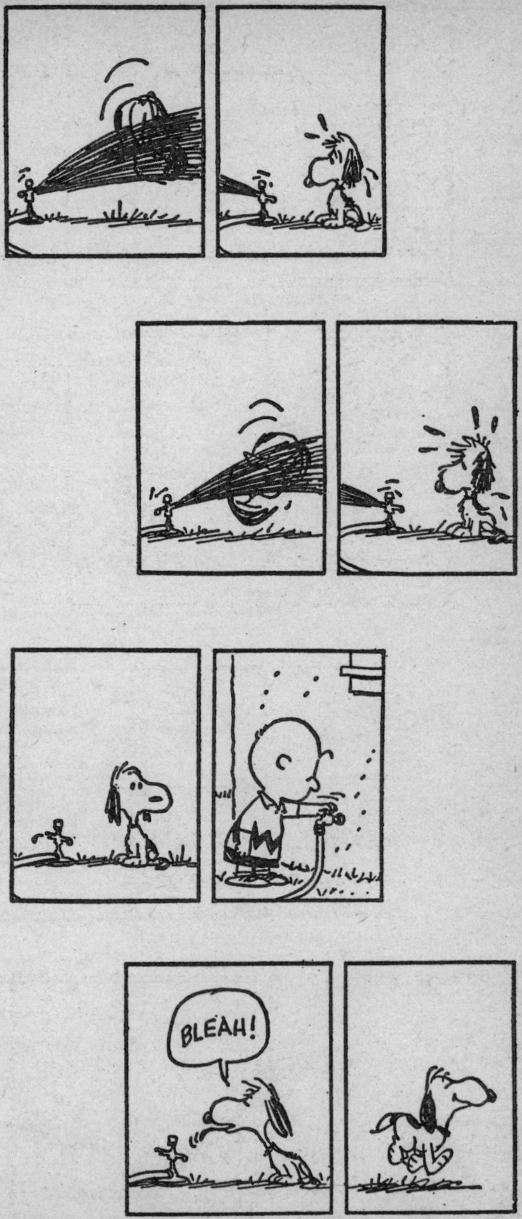
BLEAH!

WHAT A STUPID THING TO DO!

WHY DO THINGS LIKE THIS HAPPEN TO ME?

THIS IS HOPELESS!
WE GOTTA KEEP LOOKING, SNOOPY...

RATS!

I'M ALMOST AT THE POINT OF DESPAIR...
I FOUND THEM, SNOOPY! I FOUND THEM!
HERE YOU ARE..
WOW! I CAN'T BELIEVE IT!
BOY, WHAT A RELIEF....
I'M LOST WITHOUT MY CONTACT LENSES!

THIS IS NATIONAL DOG WEEK
THIS IS NATIONAL DOG WEEK
CONGRATULATIONS!

I WANT YOU TO KNOW THAT I'M BEHIND YOU ONE-HUNDRED PERCENT!
DOG WEEK
I THINK IT'S WONDERFUL WHEN A PERSON LIKE YOURSELF TAKES THE TIME TO PROMOTE SUCH A REALLY WORTH-WHILE CAUSE...
DOG WEEK
GOOD LUCK TO YOU AND YOUR ORGANIZATION
THAT SORT OF THING ALWAYS EMBARRASSES ME!

WHATEVER HAPPENED TO SUMMER?
GOOD GRIEF! I'VE NEVER BEEN SO COLD IN ALL MY LIFE!

BAM
BAM
BAM
BAM
WHY CAN'T YOU JUST SCRATCH AT THE DOOR LIKE OTHER DOGS?

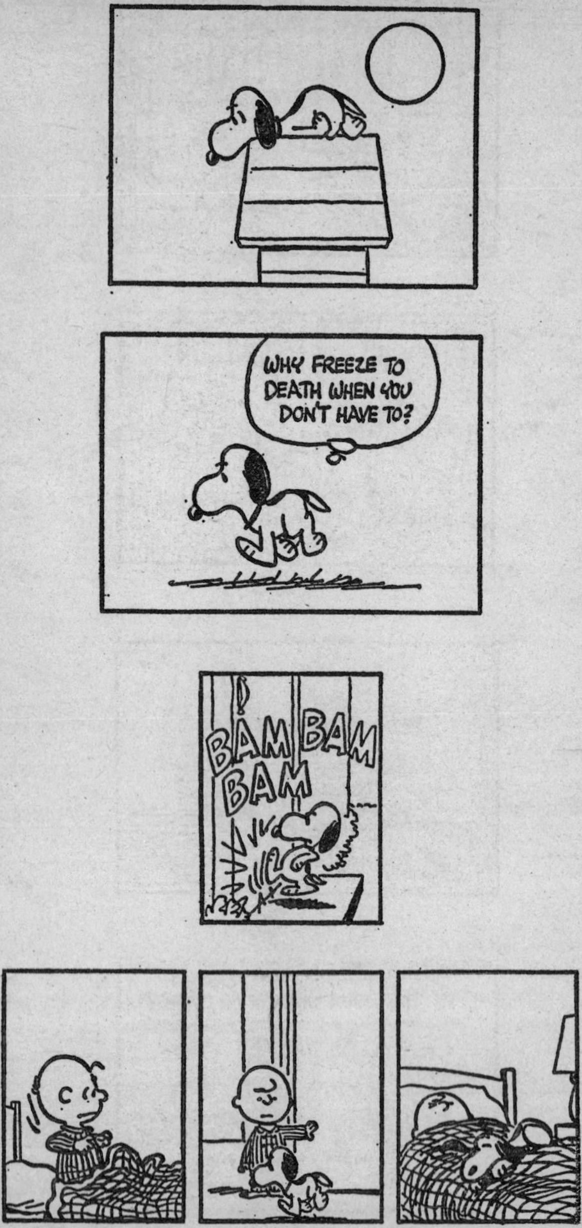
WHY FREEZE TO DEATH WHEN YOU DON'T HAVE TO?
!
BAM BAM BAM

IT'S STUFFY IN HERE..
BAM BAM BAM
GOOD GRIEF, IT'S RAINING...
BAM BAMBAM
HELLO, HUMANE SOCIETY? I HAVE A QUESTION...

BOY, I'LL BET IT WAS TEN-BELOW LAST NIGHT..
SNOW!
HEY, LINUS..C'MON OUTSIDE...IT SNOWED LAST NIGHT!

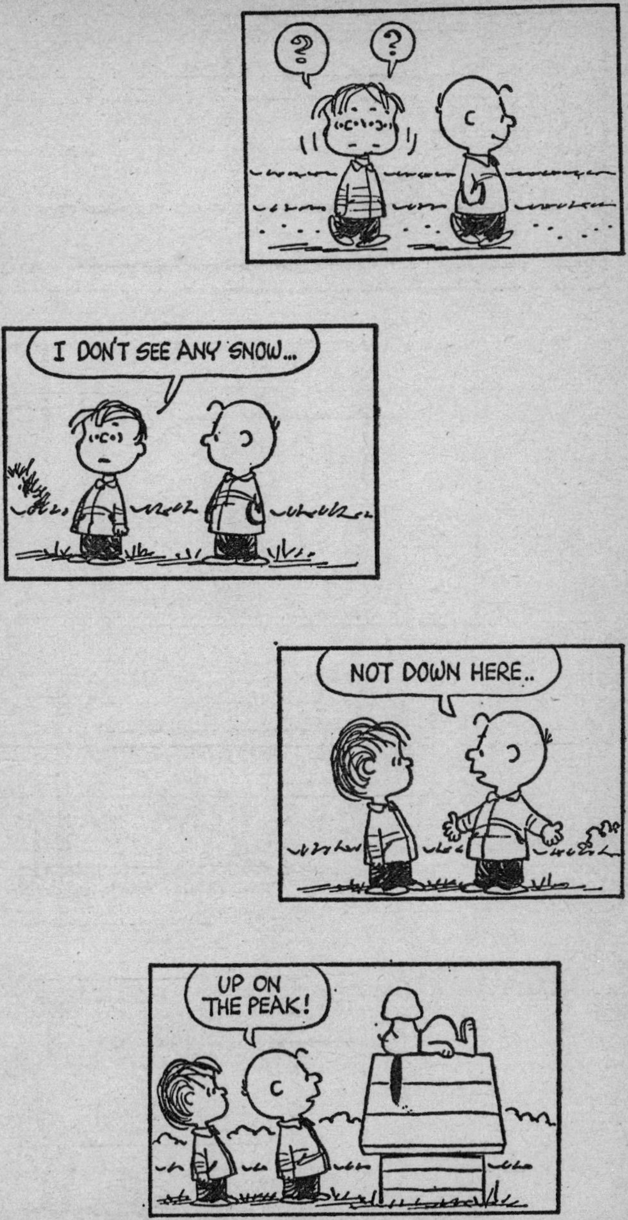
?
?
I DON'T SEE ANY SNOW...
NOT DOWN HERE..
UP ON THE PEAK!

DO YOU THINK THIS STATIONERY IS GOOD ENOUGH?
I'D HATE TO INSULT HIM BY USING CHEAP STATIONERY...
DEAR GREAT PUMPKIN,
OH, HOW I LOOK FORWARD TO YOUR ARRIVAL ON HALLOWEEN NIGHT.
WHEN YOU RISE OUT OF THE PUMPKIN PATCH, AND FLY THROUGH THE AIR, PLEASE BRING ME LOTS OF PRESENTS.

ARE YOU STILL PLANNING TO HELP ME MAIL THIS LETTER?
OF COURSE! I SAID I WOULD, AND I WILL!
MY SISTER LUCY IS GOING TO HELP ME MAIL THIS LETTER SO PLEASE BRING HER LOTS OF PRESENTS TOO.
HOW'S THAT?
FINE
GREED MAKES PEOPLE DO STRANGE THINGS..
US MAIL

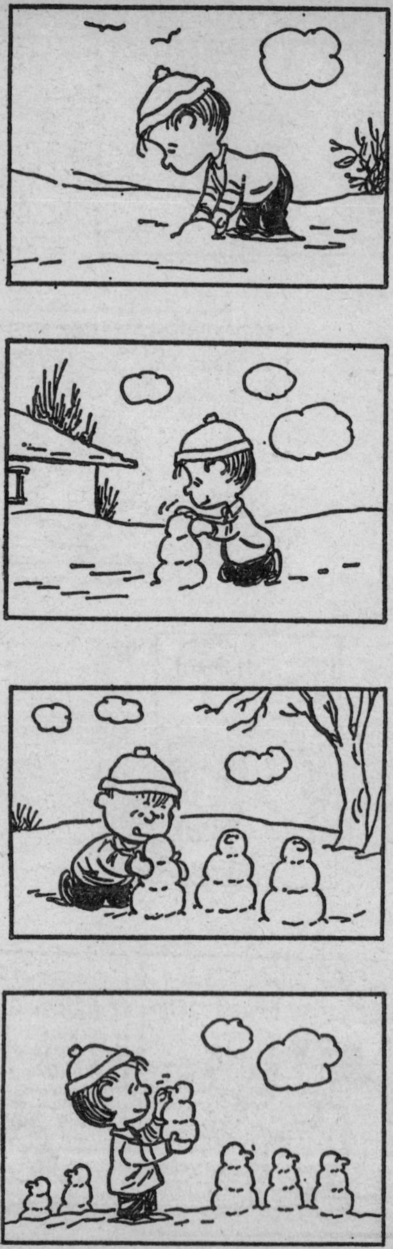

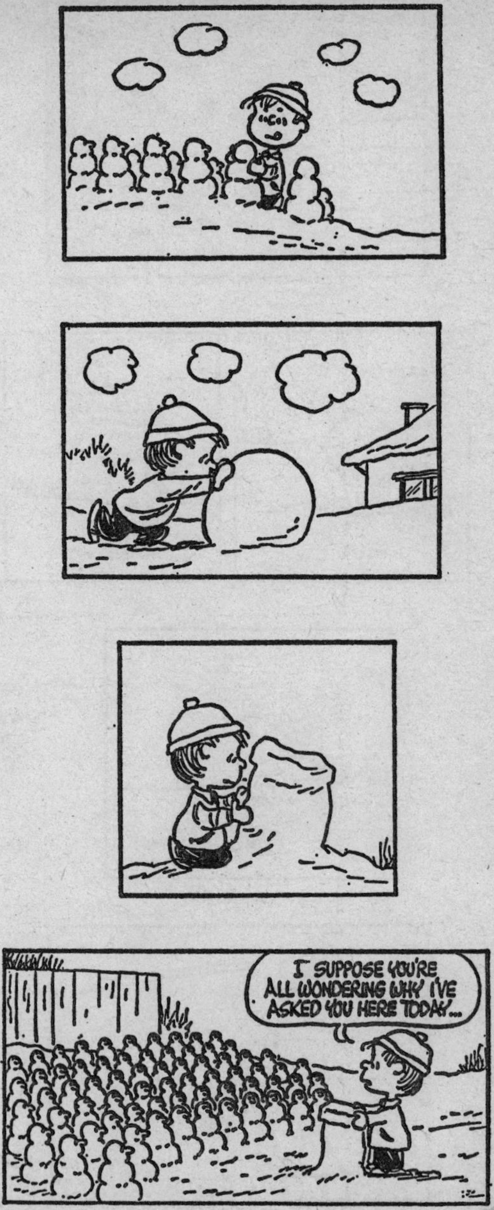
I SUPPOSE YOU'RE ALL WONDERING WHY I'VE ASKED YOU HERE TODAY...

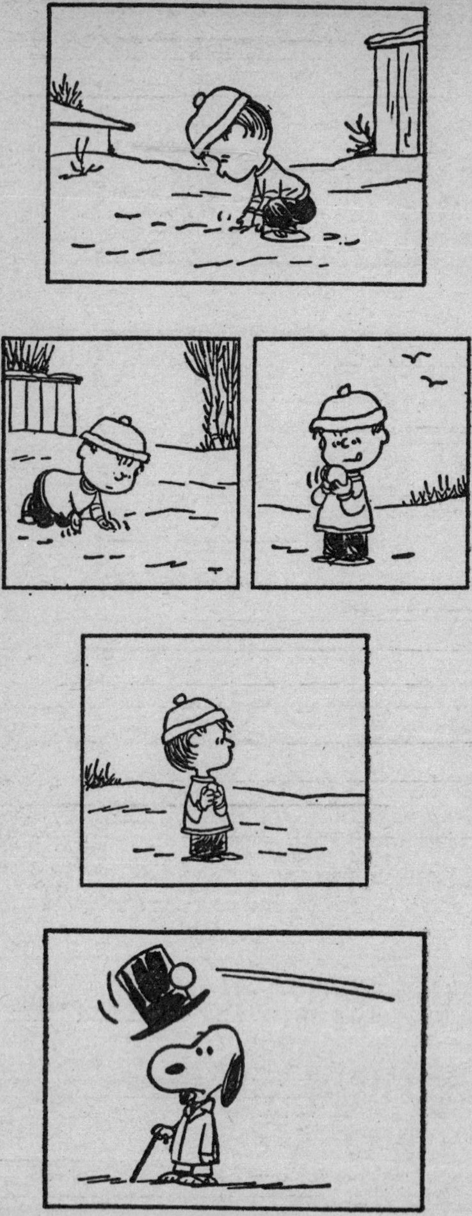

IF YOU THROW THAT SNOWBALL AT ME, I'LL HAVE THE HUMANE SOCIETY ON YOU SO FAST IT'LL MAKE YOUR HEAD SWIM!
WHOEVER PAINTS THOSE SIGNS FOR HIM, DOES A GOOD JOB!

WELL, ARE YOU GOING TO START SOMETHING, OR AREN'T YOU?
YOU THINK I'M AFRAID, DON'T YOU?
WELL, I'M NOT! WHEN IT COMES TO SNOWBALL WARS, I'M AN EXPERT!

GO AHEAD AND START SOMETHING! I'M READY FOR YOU!
C'MON! I'LL STAND THE WHOLE BUNCH OF YOU!!
WHY DO I ALWAYS SAY THINGS LIKE THAT?

AH! BREAKFAST!
I'M THE KIND WHO HAS TO EAT AS SOON AS HE GETS UP IN THE MORNING!

I DON'T BELIEVE IT!
IT'S THE MIDDLE OF JANUARY! IT'S SNOWING! THE WEATHER IS FREEZING!
AND WHAT DO I GET?
COLD CEREAL!

SAY! I LIKE THAT CAP, LUCY!
THANK YOU..
YOU'RE ALL SET FOR COLD WEATHER, AREN'T YOU?
YES, I GUESS I AM..

YOU KNOW WHAT IT'S LIKE TO BE COLD AND UNCOMFORTABLE, DON'T YOU?
OH, YES...I KNOW THAT FEELING...
YOU LIKE ANIMALS, DON'T YOU? I MEAN, YOU'VE ALWAYS BEEN SORT OF AN ANIMAL LOVER, HAVEN'T YOU?
OF COURSE!
DOGS, TOO? ESPECIALLY DOGS WHO SLEEP OUTSIDE, AND SHIVER AND SHAKE ALL NIGHT?
*SIGH*

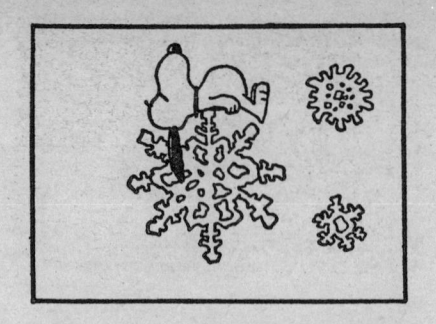

Happiness is catching snowflakes on your tongue.

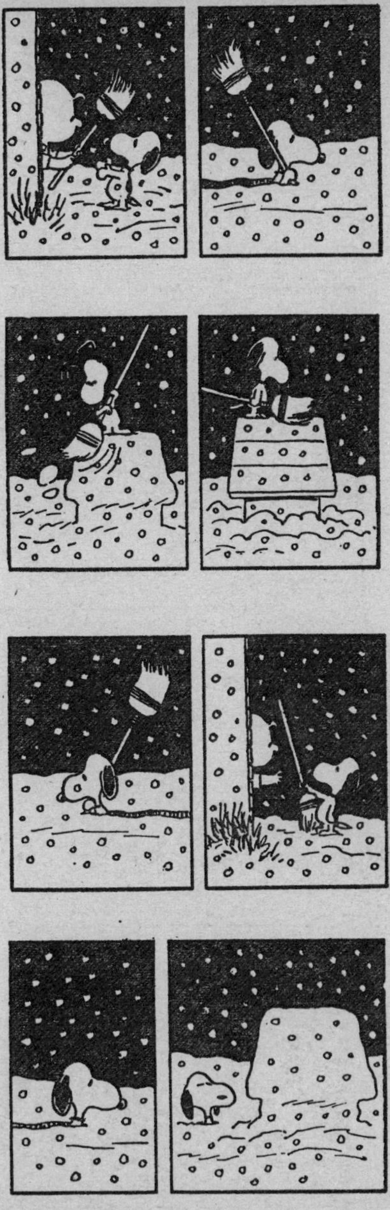

WELL, AT LEAST THE SUN IS OUT TODAY..
THAT DOESN'T MEAN I'M REALLY WARM THOUGH..
AS FAR AS I'M CONCERNED, THIS WAS THE COLDEST WINTER IN HISTORY...
I HAVEN'T BEEN WARM SINCE LAST AUGUST!

BOOT!
I'M IN NO MOOD TO LISTEN TO SOMEONE TELL ABOUT WHAT A GREAT TIME HE HAD IN BERMUDA!

PLEASE TRY TO UNDERSTAND...
SIGH
YOU'RE A FINE FELLOW, BUT I CAN'T RISK YOUR FRIENDSHIP..
EVERY TIME I BECOME CLOSE FRIENDS WITH ONE OF THESE SNOWMEN, THE SUN MELTS HIM AWAY, AND I'M LEFT BROKENHEARTED
I CAN'T STAND THE AGONY...THE TERRIBLE SENSE OF LOSS...I'VE BEEN HURT TOO OFTEN...

ALTHOUGH, I WILL ADMIT YOU HAVE BEEN A GOOD NEIGHBOR...YOU LOOK QUITE HANDSOME WITH YOUR COAL EYES AND CARROT NOSE..
OH, WELL, ONE CAN'T DELIBERATELY AVOID FRIENDSHIPS, I GUESS...
YOU CAN'T KEEP TO YOURSELF JUST BECAUSE YOU'RE AFRAID OF BEING HURT, OR...
AAUGH!
SOB
POOR SNOOPY...I SEE HE'S LOST ANOTHER FRIEND.. IT'S TOO BAD.... HE'S SO SENSITIVE...
UH, HUH... BUT I NOTICE HE WASN'T TOO SENSITIVE TO EAT THE CARROT!

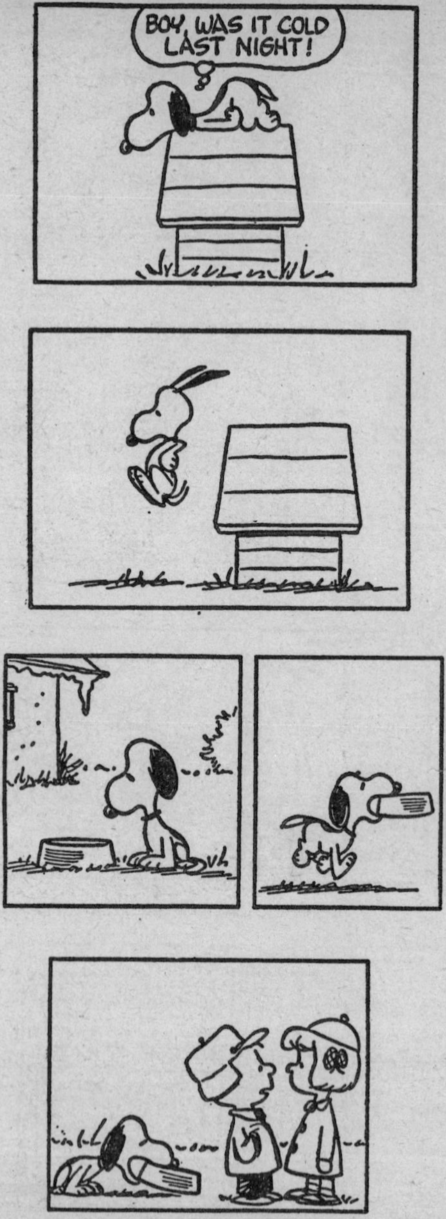
BOY, WAS IT COLD LAST NIGHT!

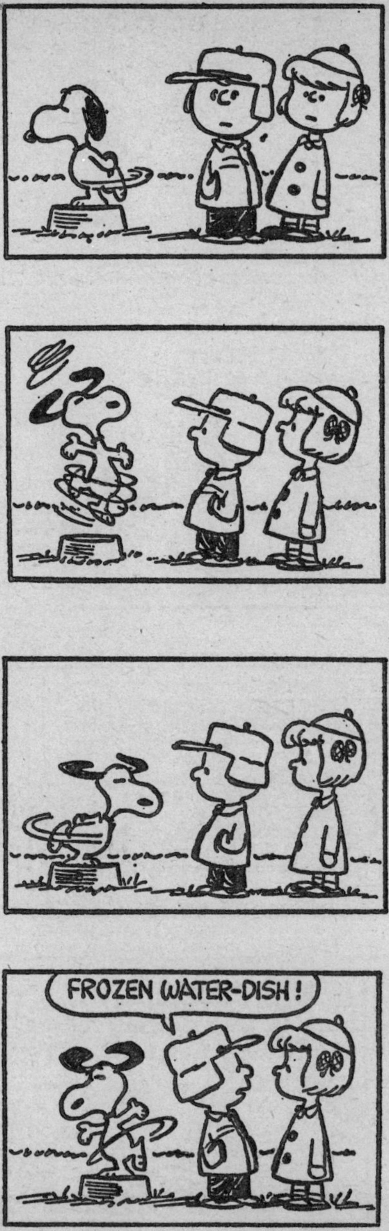
FROZEN WATER-DISH!

I SHOULDN'T BE HERE..
I SHOULD GET OUT OF LINE, AND GO HOME..
I FEEL GUILTY ABOUT GOING TO THE SHOW TODAY...I SHOULD BE HOME HELPING MY MOTHER..
ONE, PLEASE
I HAVE SCHOOLWORK TO DO, TOO...I HAVE A BOOK REPORT TO WRITE AND ABOUT TEN PAGES OF ARITHMETIC...
ONE, PLEASE

I REALLY SHOULDN'T BE GOING TO THE SHOW..I FEEL AWFULLY GUILTY ABOUT IT...I SHOULD GO HOME..
ONE, PLEASE
I CAN'T REALLY ENJOY A SHOW WHEN I FEEL GUILTY ABOUT GOING TO IT...I SHOULD JUST GET OUT OF LINE, AND GO BACK HOME..
ONE, PLEASE
ONE, PLEASE
GOOD OL' WISHY-WASHY CHARLIE BROWN..ONE, PLEASE..

HMM...
WHAT WOULD YOU DO IF I PUSHED YOUR SNOWMAN OVER?
NOTHING... WHAT **COULD** I DO?

**You're bigger and stronger than I am... you're older... you can run faster... I really couldn't do anything to stop you**

**I realize full well that I am at your mercy where things of this sort are concerned... all I can do is simply hope that you will choose not to do so...**

**Little by little I'm becoming an expert at the soft answer..**

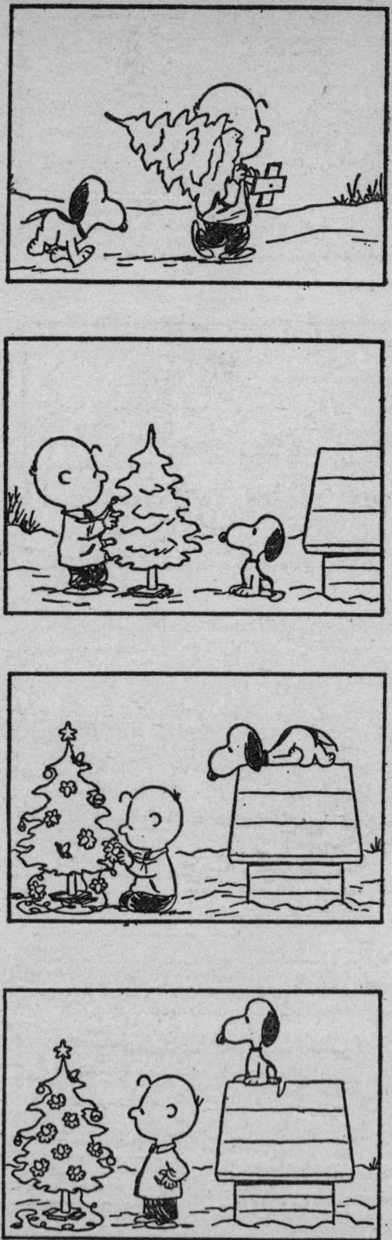

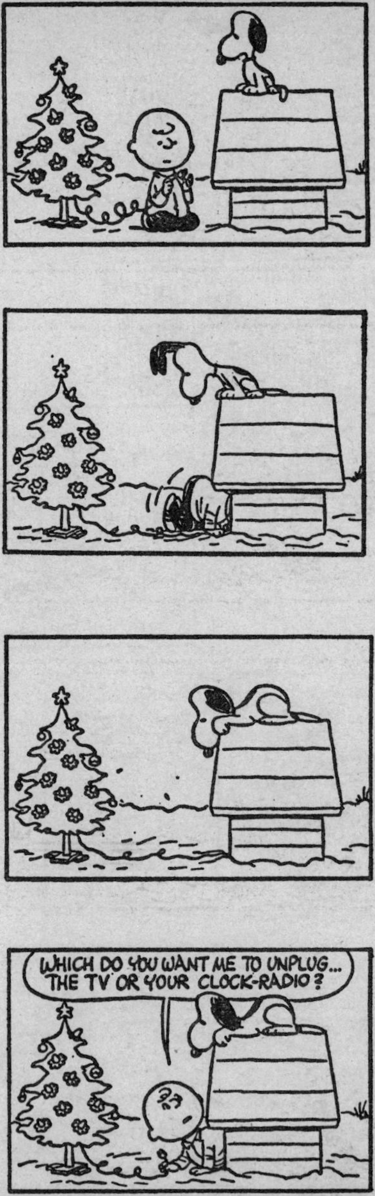
WHICH DO YOU WANT ME TO UNPLUG... THE TV OR YOUR CLOCK-RADIO?

OH, NO!
THANK YOU..
THE RAIN STOPPED, CHARLIE BROWN...WHAT DID YOU DO, CALL THE WEATHERMAN?
NO, "DIAL-A-PRAYER"!